The New Novelty Songbook

Piano Vocal Guitar

ISBN 0-88188-845-1

Hal Leonard Publishing Corporation

7777 West Bluemound Road   P.O. Box 13819   Milwaukee, Wisconsin 53213

The New Novelty Songbook

Piano Vocal Guitar

CONTENTS

ALLEY-OOP

Lively

By DALLAS FRAZIER

BABY SITTIN' BOOGIE

BALLIN' THE JACK

Words by JIM BURRIS
Music by CHRIS SMITH

Moderately

First you put your two knees close up tight,___ Then you sway 'em to the left, then you

sway 'em to the right, Step a-round the floor kind of nice and light,___ Then you

THE BUNNY HOP

By RAY ANTHONY
and LEONARD AULETTI

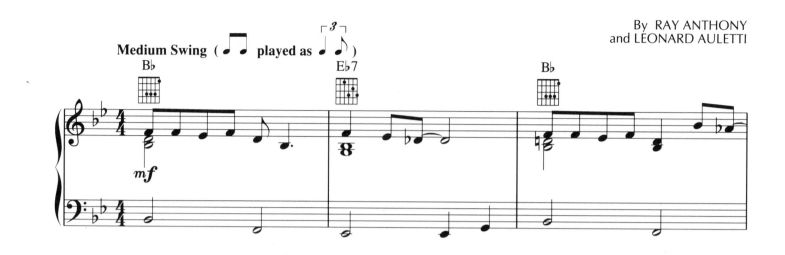

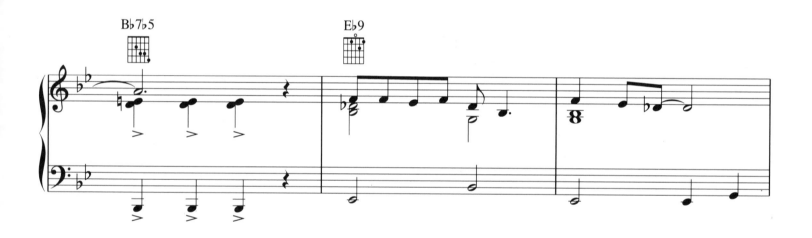

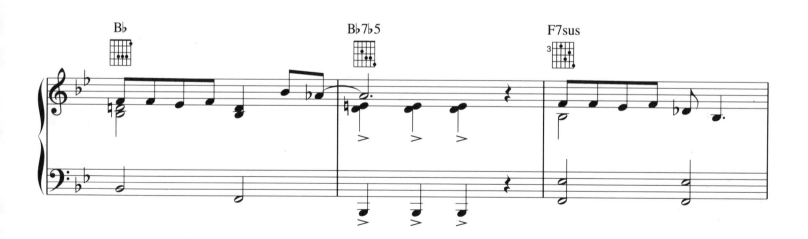

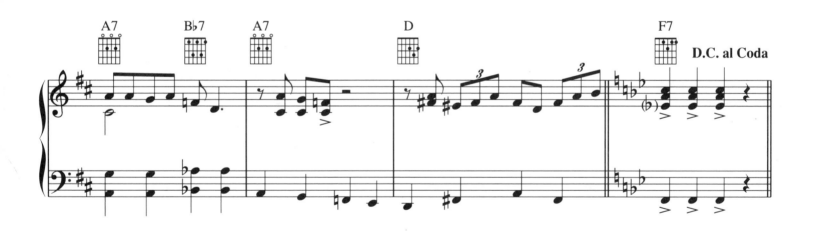

COLLEGIATE

By MOE JAFFE
and NAT BONX

Moderately

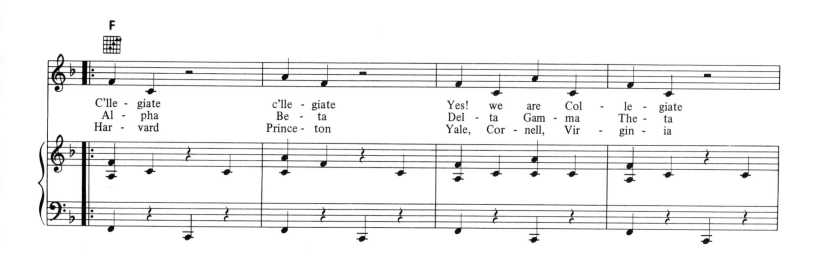

C'lle - giate   c'lle - giate   Yes! we are Col - le - giate
Al - pha   Be - ta   Del - ta Gam - ma The - ta
Har - vard   Prince - ton   Yale, Cor - nell, Vir - gin - ia

Noth - ing in - te - me - diate   No   ma'am
Lam - da Chi O - me - gu   Phi   Gam
Dart - mouth, Penn - syl - van - ia   Milk - shake

CHICKERY CHICK

Words by SYLVIA DEE
Music by SIDNEY LIPPMAN

Slowly (with an emphatic lift)

Once there lived a chick-en who would say "Chick-chick" "Chick-chick" all day.

Soon that chick got sick and tired of just "Chick-chick",— so one morn-ing he start-ed to say:

Chick-er-y Chick cha-la cha-la, check-a-la rome-y in a ba-nan-i-ka bol-li-ka wol-li-ka can't you see

CHIQUITA BANANA

Words and Music by LEN MacKENZIE,
GARTH MONTGOMERY and WILLIAM WIRGES

DANCE LITTLE BIRD

By TERRY RANDALL
and WERNER THOMAS

DUMMY SONG
(I'LL TAKE THE LEGS FROM SOME OLD TABLE)

Words and Music by LEW BROWN,
BILLY ROSE and RAY HENDERSON

GILLY GILLY OSSENFEFFER KATZENELLEN BOGEN BY THE SEA

Words and Music by AL HOFFMAN
and DICK MANNING

HELLO MUDDUH, HELLO FADDUH!
(A LETTER FROM CAMP)

Words by ALLAN SHERMAN
Music by LOU BUSCH

Medium Tempo

Hel - lo Mud - duh, Hel - lo Fad - duh, Here I am at Camp Gra - al - li -
coun-s'lors. hate the wait - ers, And the lake has

na - da; Camp is ver - y en - ter - tain - ing, and they
ga - tors; And the head - coach wants no sis - sies, so he

say we'll have some fun if it stops rain - ing. I went hik - ing with Joe
reads to us from some - thing called U - lys - ses. Now I don't want this should

HONEY BUN

(From "SOUTH PACIFIC")

Words by OSCAR HAMMERSTEIN II
Music by RICHARD RODGERS

THE HUT-SUT SONG

Words and Music by LEO V. KILLION,
TED McMICHAEL and JACK OWENS

ITSY BITSY TEENIE WEENIE YELLOW POLKA DOT BIKINI

Words and Music by PAUL J. VANCE
and LEE POCKRISS

I SCREAM-YOU SCREAM-WE ALL SCREAM FOR ICE CREAM

Words and Music by HOWARD JOHNSON,
BILLY MOLL and ROBERT KING

In the land of ice and snows Up a - mong the Es - ki - mos
Col - le - ges may come and go But the world will nev - er know

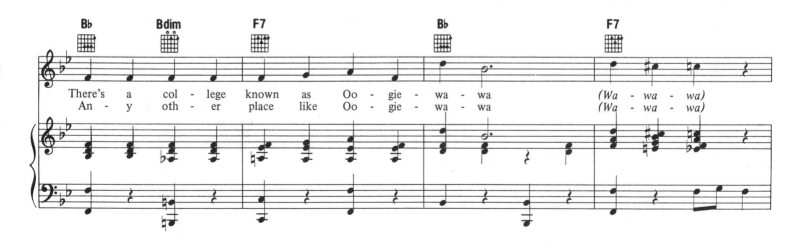

There's a col - lege known as Oo - gie - wa - wa (Wa - wa - wa)
An - y oth - er place like Oo - gie - wa - wa (Wa - wa - wa)

I'M A LONELY LITTLE PETUNIA
(In An Onion Patch)

Words by MAURIE HARTMANN and BILLY FABER
Music by MAURIE HARTMANN and JOHNNY KAMANO

I'M LOOKING OVER A FOUR LEAF CLOVER

Words by MORT DIXON
Music by HARRY WOODS

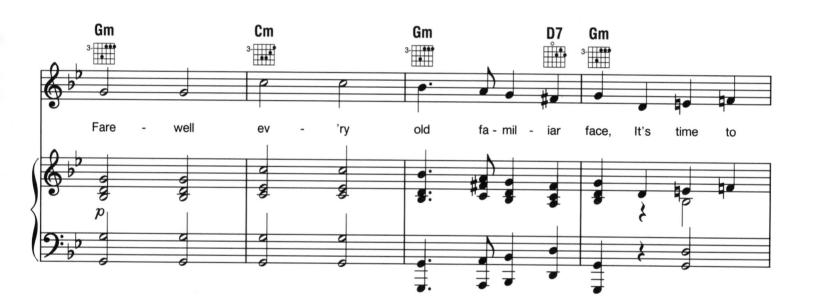

Fare - well ev - 'ry old fa - mil - iar face, It's time to

stray, _____ It's time to stray. _____

I'VE GOT A LOVELY BUNCH OF COCOANUTS

Moderately with spirit

Words and Music by FRED HEATHERTON

Down at an Eng-lish Fair_____ one eve-ning I was there,

When I heard a show-man shout-ing un-der-neath a flare.

I've Got A Lov-er-ly Bunch Of Co-coa-nuts,_____

INKA DINKA DOO

Words and Music by JIMMIE DURANTE,
BEN RYAN and HARRY DONNELY

★) Letters over diagrams are names of
the chords in original key and are
adaptable to Banjo or Guitar.

What is that haunt-ing re - frain that you hear in the air?___

___ Here and there,_____ ev -'ry - where,_____ It's just a

LITTLE TIN BOX

Words and Music by JERRY BOCK
and SHELDON HARNICK

Lyrics For LITTLE TIN BOX

FOURTH HACK
> Mr. "X," may we ask you a question?
> It's amazing is it not?
> That the city pays you slightly less
> Than fifty bucks a week
> Yet you've purchased a private yacht!

BEN
> I am positive Your Honor must be joking
> Any working man can do what I have done
> For a month or two I simply gave up smoking
> And I put my extra pennies one by one

> Into a little tin box
> A little tin box
> That a little tin key unlocks
> There is nothing unorthodox
> About a little tin box

MEN
> About a little tin box
> About a little tin box

> In a little tin box
> A little tin box
> That a little tin key unlocks

BEN
> There is honor and purity

ALL
> Lots of security
> In a little tin box

FIFTH HACK *(Speaking)* Next witness.

FIRST HACK
> Mr. "Y," we've been told You don't feel well
> And we know you've lost your voice
> But we wonder how you managed on the salary you make
> To acquire a new Rolls Royce

BEN
> You're implying I'm a crook and I say no sir!
> There is nothing in my past I care to hide
> I've been taking empty bottles to the grocer
> And each nickel that I got was put aside

MEN
> That he got was put aside

BEN
> Into a little tin box
> A little tin box
> That a little tin key unlocks
> There is nothing unorthodox
> About a little tin box

MEN
> About a little tin box
> About a little tin box
> In a little tin box
> A little tin box
> There's a cushion for life's rude shocks

BEN
> There is faith, hope and charity

ALL
> Hard-won prosperity
> In a little tin box.

FIFTH HACK *(Speaking)* Next witness! Take the stand!

SIXTH HACK
> Mr. "Z," you're a junior official
> And your income's rather low
> Yet you've kept a dozen women
> In the very best hotels
> Would you kindly explain, how so?

BEN
> I can see Your Honor doesn't pull his punches
> And it looks a trifle fishy, I'll admit
> But for one whole week I went without my lunches
> And it mounted up, Your Honor, bit by bit

MEN
> Up Your Honor, bit by bit.
> It's just a little tin box
> A little tin box
> That a little tin key unlocks

> There is nothing unorthodox
> About a little tin box
> About a little tin box
> In a little tin box
> A little tin box
> All a-glitter with blue chip stocks

BEN
> There is something delectable

ALL
> Almost respectable
> In a little tin box
> In a little tin box!

MAH-NA MAH-NA

By PIERO UMILIANI

MAIRZY DOATS

By MILTON DRAKE, AL HOFFMAN,
and JERRY LIVINGSTON

MONSTER MASH

Words and Music by BOBBY PICKETT
and LEONARD CAPIZZI

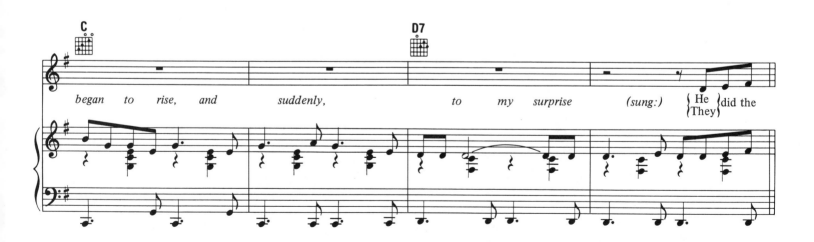

2. From my laboratory in the castle east.
   To the master bedroom where the vampires feast.
   The ghouls all came from their humble abodes
   To catch a jolt from my electrodes.
   (to Chorus: They did the mash)

3. The zombies were having fun,
   The party had just begun.
   The guests included Wolf-man,
   Dracula, and his son.

4. The scene was rockin'; all were digging the sounds,
   Igor on chains, backed by his baying hounds.
   The coffin-bangers were about to arrive
   With their vocal group "The Crypt-Kicker Five"
   (to Chorus: They played the mash)

5. Out from his coffin, Drac's voice did ring;
   Seems he was troubled by just one thing.
   He opened the lid and shook his fist,
   And said, "Whatever happened to my Transylvanian twist?"
   (to Chorus: It's now the mash)

6. Now everything's cool, Drac's a part of the band
   And my monster mash is the hit of the land.
   For you, the living, this mash was meant too,
   When you get to my door, tell them Boris sent you. (till fade)
   (to Chorus: And you can mash)

MY ATTORNEY, BERNIE

Arranged for Piano by DAVID FRISHBERG

Words and Music by
DAVID FRISHBERG

Na Na Hey Hey Kiss Him Goodbye

Words and Music by GARY DeCARLO,
PAUL LEKA and DALE FRASHUER

OPEN THE DOOR, RICHARD!

Words by "DUSTY" FLETCHER and JOHN MASON
Music by JACK McVEA and DAN HOWELL

PADDLIN' MADELIN' HOME

Words and Music by
HARRY WOODS

RAMA LAMA DING DONG

Words and Music by
GEORGE JONES, JR.

PURPLE PEOPLE EATER

Words and Music by SHEB WOOLEY

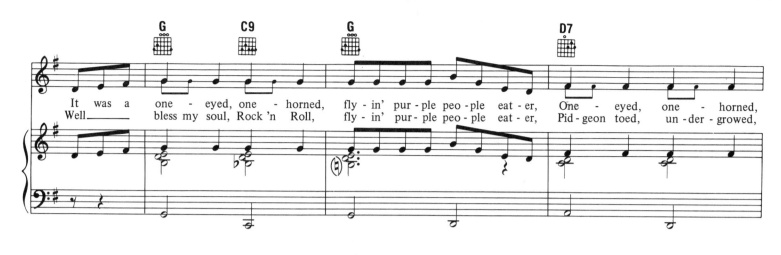

It was a one-eyed, one-horned, fly-in' pur-ple peo-ple eat-er, One-eyed, one-horned,
Well_____ bless my soul, Rock 'n Roll, fly-in' pur-ple peo-ple eat-er, Pid-geon toed, un-der-growed,

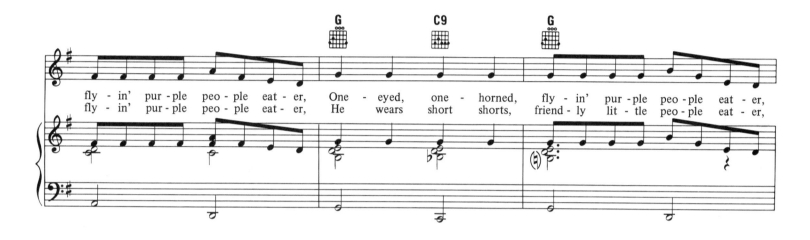

fly-in' pur-ple peo-ple eat-er, One-eyed, one-horned, fly-in' pur-ple peo-ple eat-er,
fly-in' pur-ple peo-ple eat-er, He wears short shorts, friend-ly lit-tle peo-ple eat-er,

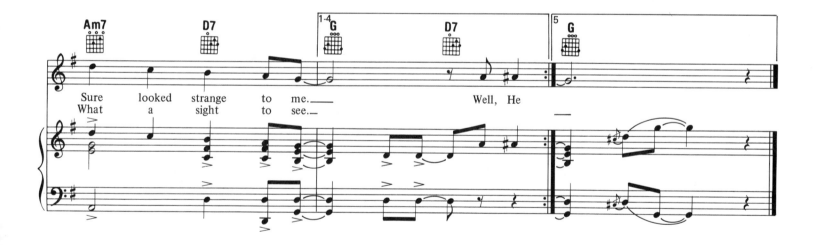

Sure looked strange to me.___ Well, He
What a sight to see.___

3. I said, "Mister purple people eater, what's your line?"
He said, "Eatin' purple people, and it sure is fine,
But that's not the reason that I came to land,
I wanna get a job in a rock and roll band."

4. And then he swung from the tree and he lit on the ground,
And he started to rock, a-really rockin' around.
It was a crazy ditty with a swingin' tune,
Singa bop bapa loop a lap a loom bam boom.

5. Well he went on his way and then what-a you know,
I saw him last night on a T.V. show,
He was blowin' it out, really knockin' 'em dead.
Playin' rock 'n' roll music thru the horn in his head.

RAG MOP

Words and Music by JOHNNIE LEE WILLS
and DEACON ANDERSON

Medium Bounce

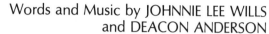

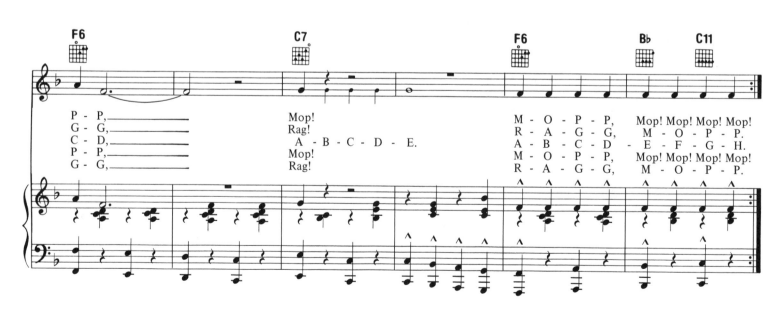

Chorus—*After 2nd and 5th Verses*

SAM, YOU MADE THE PANTS TOO LONG

Words by FRED WHITEHOUSE and MILTON BERLE
Adapted from "Lord You Made The Night too Long"
by SAM M. LEWIS and VICTOR YOUNG

SHOO FLY PIE AND APPLE PAN DOWDY

Words by SAMMY GALLOP
Music by GUY WOOD

Slow bounce

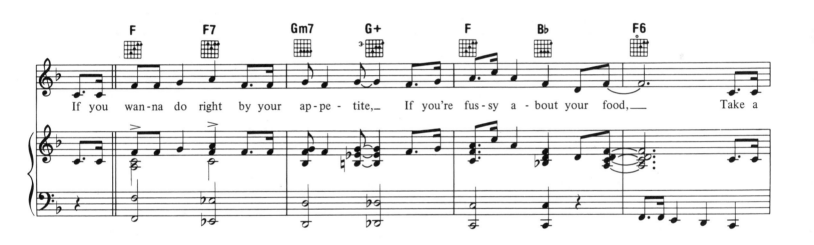

If you wan-na do right by your ap-pe-tite,__ If you're fus-sy a-bout your food,__ Take a

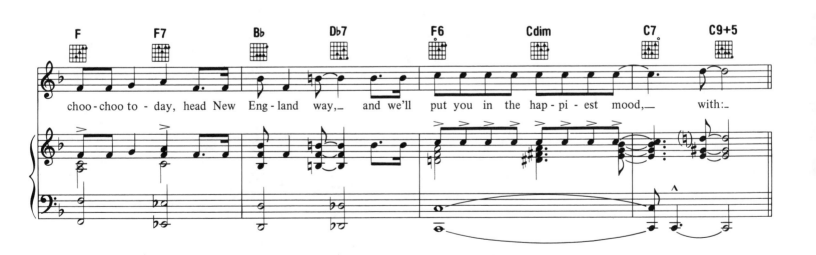

choo-choo to-day, head New Eng-land way,__ and we'll put you in the hap-pi-est mood,__ with:__

SUPERCALIFRAGILISTICEXPIALIDOCIOUS

(From Walt Disney's "MARY POPPINS")

Words and Music by RICHARD M. SHERMAN
and ROBERT B. SHERMAN

SWEET VIOLETS

Words and Music by CY COBEN
and CHARLES GREAN

barn where he gave her a lec - ture on
fath - er, and he called a tax - i and
plan - ning for his wed - ding suit which he

hors - es and chick - ens and eggs, and told her that
got there be - fore ver - y long, 'cause some - one was
pur - chased for on - ly one buck, but then he found

she had such beau - ti - ful man - ners that
do - ing such his lit - tle girl right for a
out he was just out of mon - ey and

suit - ed a girl of her charms, a girl that he
change and so that's why he said: If you mar - ry
so he got left in the lurch, stand - ing and

THE THING

Words and Music by
CHARLES R. GREAN

Moderately Bright

Chorus

1. While I was walk-ing down the beach one bright and sun-ny day, ___ I
2. (I) picked it up and ran to town as hap-py as a king. ___ I

saw a great big wood-en box a-float-in' in the bay. ___ I
took it to a guy I know who'd buy most an-y-thing. ___ But

pulled it in and o-pened it up and much to my sur-
this is what he hol-lered at me as I walked in his

3) I turned around and got right out a-runnin' for my life,
And then I took it home with me to give it to my wife.
But this is what she hollered at me as I walked in the door:
Oh, get out of here with that xxx and don't come back no more.
Oh, get out of here with that xxx and don't come back no more.

4) I wandered all around the town until I chanced to meet
A hobo who was looking for a handout on the street.
He said he'd take most any old thing, he was a desperate man,
But when I showed him the xxx, he turned around and ran.
Oh, when I showed him the xxx, he turned around and ran.

5) I wandered on for many years, a victim of my fate,
Until one day I came upon Saint Peter at the gate.
And when I tried to take it inside he told me where to go:
Get out of here with that xxx and take it down below.
Oh, get out of here with that xxx and take it down below.

6) The moral of the story is if you're out on the beach
And you should see a great big box and it's within your reach,
Don't ever stop and open it up, that's my advice to you,
'Cause you'll never get rid of the xxx, no matter what you do.
Oh, you'll never get rid of the xxx, no matter what you do.

110

(Boop-Boop Dit-tem Dat-tem What-tem Chu!)
THREE LITTLE FISHIES
(Itty Bitty Poo)

Words and Music by
SAXIE DOWELL

Brightly

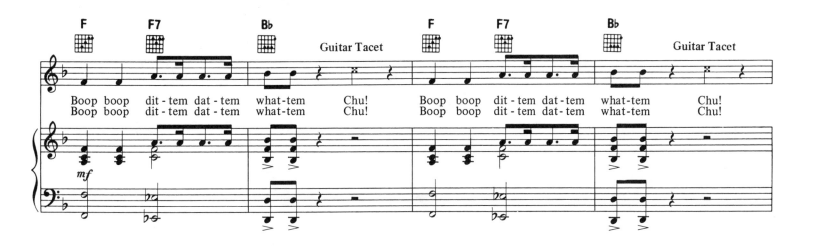

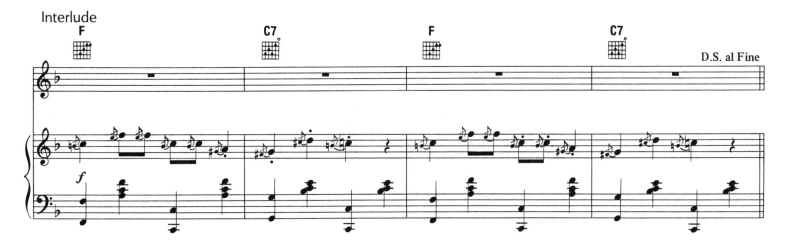

3rd Chorus
"Whee!" yelled the little fishies, "Here's a lot of fun,
We'll swim in the sea till the day is done."
They swam and they swam and it was a lark,
Till all of a sudden they met a SHARK!

("Whee!" 'elled de itty fitties "Ears a wot of fun,
Ee'll fim in de fee ill de day is un."
Dey fam and dey fam and it was a wark,
Till aw of a tudden dey taw a TARK!)

Boop boop dit-tem dot-tem what-tem Chu!
"   "   "   "   "   "   "   "   "   "
        "   "   "   "   "   "   "   "   "

Till aw of a tudden dey taw a TARK!

4th Chorus
"Help!" cried the little fishies, "Gee! look at all the whales!"
And quick as they could they turned on their tails.
And back to the pool in the meadow they swam,
And they swam and they swam back over the dam.

("He'p!" tied de itty fitties, "Dee! ook at all de fales!"
And twit as dey tood dey turned on deir tails!
And bat to de poo in de meddy dey fam,
And dey fam and dey fam bat over de dam.)

Boop boop dit-tem dot-tem what-tem Chu!
"   "   "   "   "   "   "   "   "   "
        "   "   "   "   "   "   "   "   "

And dey fam and dey fam bat over de dam.

TOO FAT POLKA

By ROSS MacLEAN and ARTHUR RICHARDSON

Dm7 G7 C Cdim G7

dan - cing _____ With my Jum - Jum - Jum - bo I don't want her,
lose - some _____ I would like her more - some

G7 C C#dim G7sus G7

you can have her, she's too fat for me She's too fat for me

C G7 C

She's too fat for me I don't want her, you can have her, she's too fat for

F G7 C G7 [1 C Cdim]

me She's too fat, she's too fat she's too fat for me. Oh!

[2 C To Trio] [3 C Last]

me. _____ me. _____

Trio

Can she prance up a hill? No! No! No! No!
No! Can she dance a qua - drille? No! No!
No! No! No! Does she fit in my *coupe?
By her - self she's a group Could she pos - si - bly
Sit up - on my knee? No! No! No! Oh!

*pronounced "coop"

To last 16 bars of Chorus -

WHERE DID ROBINSON CRUSOE GO WITH FRIDAY ON SATURDAY NIGHT?

Words by SAM M. LEWIS and JOE YOUNG
Music by GEO. W. MEYER

WOOLY BULLY

Words and Music by
DOMINGO SAMUDIO

2. **Hatty told Matty**
   Let's don't take no chance,
   Let's not be L 7
   Come and learn to dance
   Wooly bully - wooly bully
   Wooly bully - wooly bully - wooly bully.

3. **Matty told Hatty**
   That's the thing to do,
   Get yo' someone really
   To pull the wool with you-
   Wooly bully - wooly bully
   Wooly bully - wooly bully - wooly bully.

YAKETY YAK

Words and Music by JERRY LEIBER
and MIKE STOLLER

YES! WE HAVE NO BANANAS

By FRANK SILVER and IRVING COHN

VAN LINGLE MUNGO

Arranged for Piano by DAVID FRISHBERG

Words and Music by
DAVID FRISHBERG